Dear Parents,

Welcome to the Scholastic Reader series. We have taken over 80 years of experience with teachers, parents, and children and put it into a program that is designed to match your child's interests and skills.

Level 1—Short sentences and stories made up of words kids can sound out using their phonics skills and words that are important to remember.

Level 2—Longer sentences and stories with words kids need to know and new "big" words that they will want to know.

Level 3—From sentences to paragraphs to longer stories, these books have large "chunks" of text and are made up of a rich vocabulary.

Level 4—First chapter books with more words and fewer pictures.

It is important that children learn to read well enough to succeed in school and beyond. Here are ideas for reading this book with your child:

- Look at the book together. Encourage your child to read the title and make a prediction about the story.
- Read the book together. Encourage your child to sound out words when appropriate. When your child struggles, you can help by providing the word.
- Encourage your child to retell the story. This is a great way to check for comprehension.

Scholastic Readers are designed to support your child's efforts to learn how to read at every age and every stage. Enjoy helping your child learn to read and love to read.

—**Francie Alexander**
Chief Education Officer
Scholastic Education

Ms. Frizzle

Liz

Written by Anne Capeci
Illustrated by Carolyn Bracken

Sincere appreciation to Jonathan D.W. Kahl, Professor of Atmospheric
Science at the University of Wisconsin-Milwaukee, for his advice in the
preparation of the manuscript and illustrations.
Based on *The Magic School Bus* books
written by Joanna Cole and illustrated by Bruce Degen.

0-439-80108-7

12 11 10   9/0 10/0

Designed by Rick DeMonico.

Printed in the U.S.A.   First printing, April 2006

The Magic School Bus
Rides the Wind

nold   Ralphie   Keesha   Phoebe   Carlos   Tim   Wanda   Dorothy Ann

SCHOLASTIC INC.

New York Toronto London Auckland Sydney
Mexico City New Delhi Hong Kong Buenos Aires

Today we are learning about wind.
Outside, leaves are blowing.
"This wind is just right for flying
kites," Ms. Frizzle says. "Let's go!"

WINDY WORDS:

The wind...
blows
gusts
howls
whispers
whistles

WHAT IS WIND?
by Dorothy Ann

Wind is air that
moves. Wind is caused
when heavy air pushes
into lighter air.
Wind can go up, down,
and around.

WIND CHART		
DAY	STRENGTH	DIRECT
MON	12 mph	NW
TUES	2 mph	SE
WED	4 mph	SW
THU	10 mph	NW
FRI	3 mph	SE
SAT		
SU		

I AM WRITING A STORY ABOUT WIND.

YOU CAN DO IT LATER.

Ms. Frizzle gets a twinkle in her eye.
"I know how," she says.
"Let's get on the bus!"

We get into the Magic School Bus.
The bus starts to change.
It becomes a hang glider.
Ms. Frizzle says it will catch the wind
just like a kite.

Now the wind lifts us into the sky!

We are not the only ones flying on the wind.

WIND MAKES THINGS GO
by Phoebe

When wind pushes on things, it makes them go up.

KITE

HANG GLIDER

It makes them go forward.

SAILBOAT

And round and round, too.

WINDMILL

ALL ABOUT
WEATHER BALLOONS
by Ralphie

Weather balloons can
go 20 miles high. They
have tools that tell us
what the weather is like
way up in the sky.

WIND ENERGY
by Keesha

Windmills use the wind to help us.

Wind makes the blades spin.

The spinning makes a machine that is inside do work.

Some windmills grind grain. Some pump water. And some windmills make electricity.

BLADES
catch wind and spin

GENERATOR
Converts energy to electricity

COMPUTER SYSTEM
Controls blade direction

CABLE
carries electricity to line

Wanda's kite is safe and sound.
The Magic School Bus is ready to go.
We are ready, too.

HOW WE MEASURE WIND

We use special tools to measure wind:
An anemometer measures the speed of wind.

A wind sock shows how strong the wind is.
It shows which way the wind is going, too.